Vishnu and Garuda the Eagle

Shubha Vilas

An imprint of Om Books International

Garuda was the son of Vinata and Sage Kashyap. He was half-human and half-eagle. He had the face, beak, wings and talons of an eagle, but the body of a human.

Once Vinata lost a bet with her sister and co-wife, Kadru. Kadru actually cheated and made Vinata her slave.

Garuda was deeply saddened by his mother's plight and wanted desperately to free his mother from the bondage of Kadru. Therefore, he agreed to bring amrit or sweet nectar from Devalok, which would make Kadru and her snake sons powerful and immortal.

Garuda had agreed to do what no one had ever done before. He would try with his heart and soul to steal the heavenly nectar from Indraloka. It was a deadly mission. One that could even end his life. But he had to try for the sake of his mother's freedom.

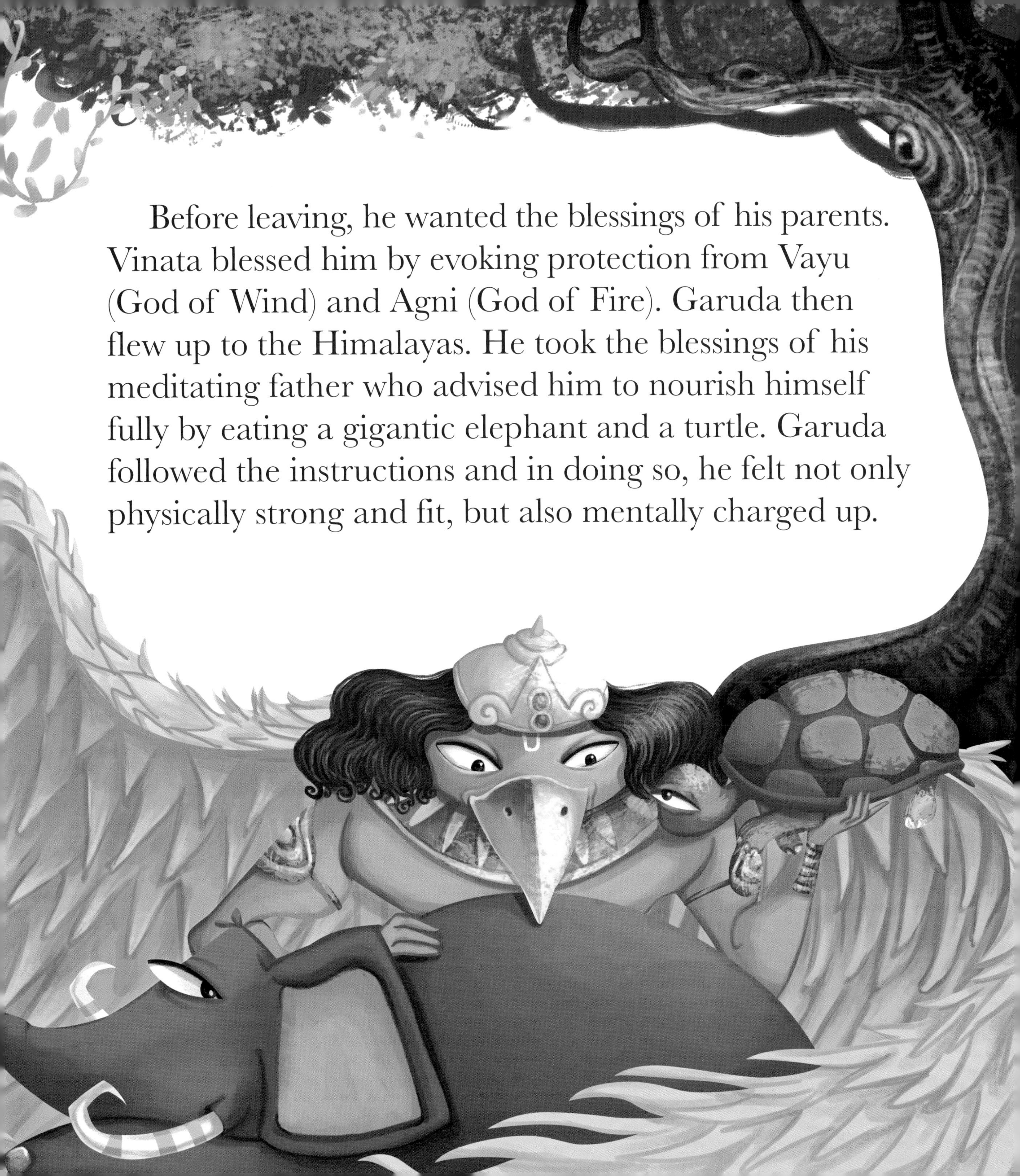

Before leaving, he wanted the blessings of his parents. Vinata blessed him by evoking protection from Vayu (God of Wind) and Agni (God of Fire). Garuda then flew up to the Himalayas. He took the blessings of his meditating father who advised him to nourish himself fully by eating a gigantic elephant and a turtle. Garuda followed the instructions and in doing so, he felt not only physically strong and fit, but also mentally charged up.

Garuda reached Indraloka, his destination, where the nectar was kept. But he was taken aback to see that it was guarded heavily by a huge army. How could a lone eagle ever defeat an army of millions? But the determined Garuda didn't want to give up and go back home. The thought of breaking his mother's heart stopped him from even thinking in that direction.

He gathered his courage and decided to fight the battle with his brain. He flapped his huge wings and raised a dust storm. The storm that began as a little air soon turned into a hurricane that blew off the entire army. In no time, he had wiped out an army that would have taken anyone else days, if not weeks, to fight with.

Once that was done, he stepped into the wall that gave entry to the devalok (heaven). But the inner chamber was fiery hot. To reach the nectar, he had to cross a wall of fire. And risk getting roasted, too.

Suddenly, he knew what to do. He flew back all the way to Earth and dived into the ocean. He scooped up litres and litres of water in his beak, returned quickly, and doused the flames.

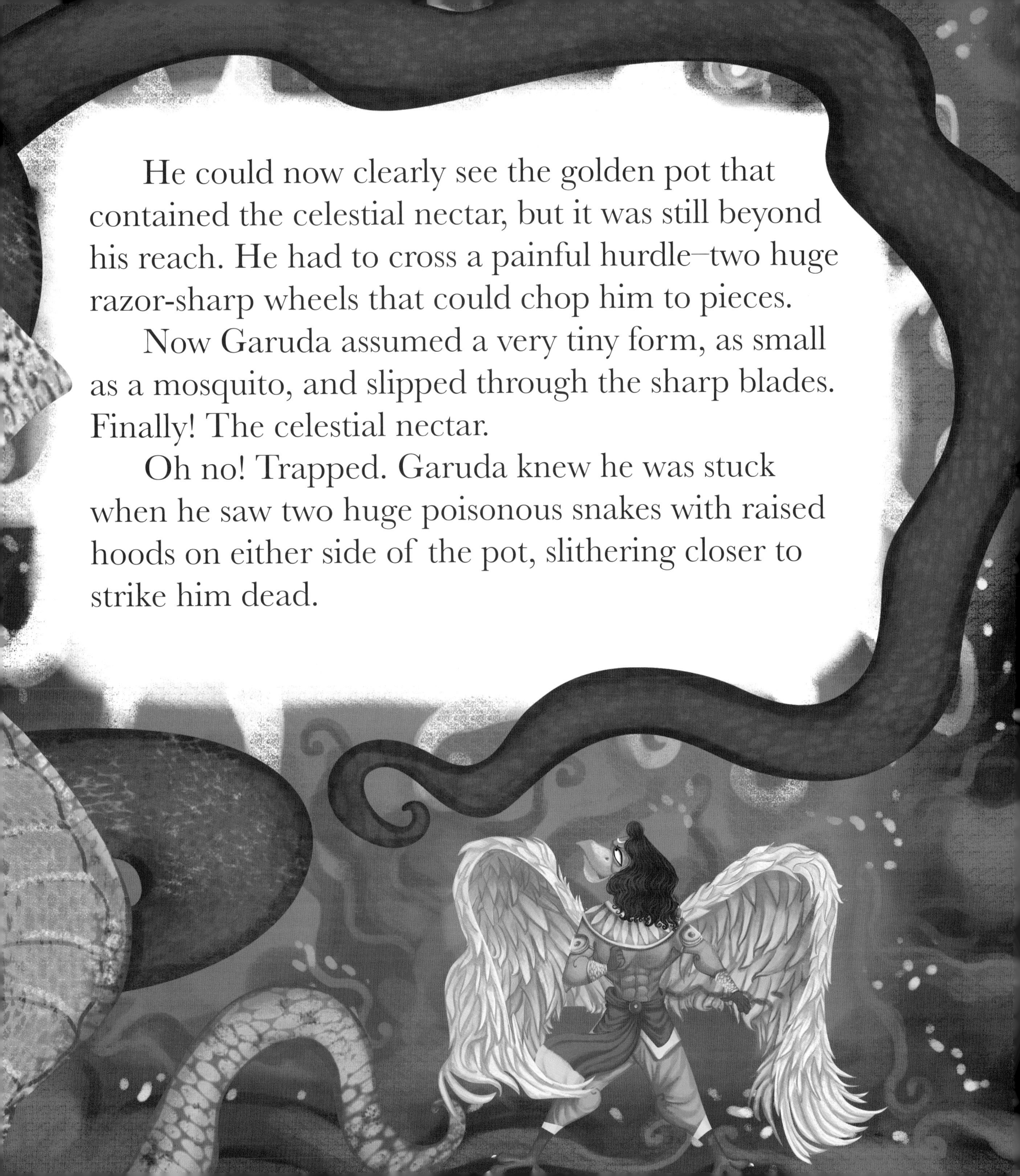

He could now clearly see the golden pot that contained the celestial nectar, but it was still beyond his reach. He had to cross a painful hurdle–two huge razor-sharp wheels that could chop him to pieces.

Now Garuda assumed a very tiny form, as small as a mosquito, and slipped through the sharp blades. Finally! The celestial nectar.

Oh no! Trapped. Garuda knew he was stuck when he saw two huge poisonous snakes with raised hoods on either side of the pot, slithering closer to strike him dead.

Garuda quickly began flapping his wings with as much power as he could and as fast as he could. The strong wind from Garuda's wings flung the snakes out of the pots on to the metal discs. The metal discs did a clean job of slicing them to pieces.

Now the challenge was to carry the pot of nectar with the discs rotating around him. Garuda then began to expand himself. As he grew larger and larger, the metal discs shattered into pieces, and he scooped away the pot of nectar and flew out of the heavens down towards Earth.

On the way, he met Indra. Indra was extremely shocked that someone could steal the nectar so easily from his kingdom. Seeing that he wouldn't be able to defeat Garuda in a combat, he begged Garuda not to give the nectar to the serpents. Garuda agreed to return the nectar once his mother was free.

Meanwhile, Vishnu was watching Garuda minutely. Impressed with his intelligence, his compassion, and his desire to serve his mother, Vishnu made an offer.

'Will you be my carrier, Garuda?' Garuda was delighted and accepted the fantastic offer.

Garuda had begun the adventure with the aim of freeing his mother from slavery. That selfless act gave him a chance to serve Lord Vishnu. It had helped him soar into the life of Lord Vishnu and find his purpose in life.